Also available
by *Laurence and Catherine Anholt*

Sun Snow Stars Sky
All About You
One, Two, Three, Count With Me
Animals Animals All Around

by Catherine Anholt
When I Was a Baby
Tom's Rainbow Walk

For Daniel

Look What
I Can Do

Look What I Can Do

Catherine and Laurence Anholt

Everyone can do something.

 What things can you do by yourself?

I can whistle.

I can push the pram.

I can write my name.

I can wash my own hair.

I can make a LOT of noise.
What things can YOU do?

Some things are hard when you are small.
But they get easier as you grow bigger.

I can sit.

I can crawl.

I can stand.

I can run.

I can jump.

I can swing.

I can throw.

I can bounce.

I can catch.

I can swim.

There's only one thing I can't do -
I just can't fly a kite.

I can get dressed all by myself.

Some things are difficult like

buttons, zips, and shoes.

Other things are easy like

hats, socks, boots

and slippers.

I can brush my teeth

and my hair.

Some of us don't have any hair at all!

Some of us have lots.

The more I try the easier things get . . .

I can make
a model.

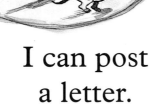

I can post
a letter.

I can
grow things.

I can
cook.

I can stick
things together.

I can do
a puzzle.

I can build a tower.

I can dig a hole.

I can thread beads.

I can cut with scissors.

I can tidy away afterwards.

But I just wish I could fly my kite.

I can use a knife and fork and a spoon.

I can drink from a cup.

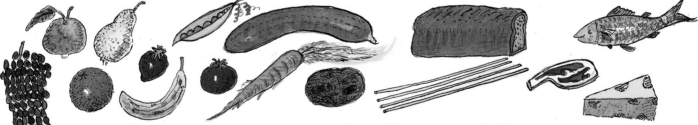

I can eat lots of different things.

I can drink milk, juice and even water.

I can try all kinds of new foods.

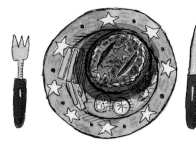

pizza

pasta

hot dog

salad

spaghetti

egg on toast

I can stay at the table.

I can go to the toilet all by myself.

I can use my potty.

I can use toilet paper
(but not miles and miles).

I can flush the toilet and wash
my hands afterwards.

But I don't get worried if accidents happen.

Every day I learn something new . . .

I can draw.

I can count.

I can work on
a computer.

I can nearly
tell the time.

I can say my ABC.

I can read a book.

I can play the drums.

But no matter how I try
I just can't FLY THAT KITE!

When I think about it,
there must be MILLIONS of things I can do . . .

I can take the top off my egg.

I can make a collection.

I can sleep right through the night.

I can wobble my tooth.

I can blow my nose.

I can make a birthday card.

I can help with the shopping.

I can choose the right clothes for the weather.

I can put on a stamp the right way up.

I can remember a rhyme.

I can walk in my mum's shoes.

I can suck my toes.

I can balance on one leg.

I can clap my hands.

I can blow bubbles.

I can run up a hill
and roll down again.

I can talk in a funny voice.

I can touch my toes.

I can make a   monster face.

I can wag my tail.

In fact, there's only one thing I can't do . . .
I JUST CAN'T FLY MY KITE!

Sometimes things seem almost impossible.

But if I try

try

try

try again . . .

I can do just about ANYTHING AT ALL.

First published in Great Britain 1998
by Mammoth
an imprint of Reed International Books Ltd
Michelin House, 81 Fulham Road, London SW3 6RB
10 9 8 7 6 5 4 3 2 1
Copyright © Catherine and Laurence Anholt 1998
Catherine and Laurence Anholt have asserted their moral rights
ISBN 0 7497 3423 X

A CIP catalogue record for this title is available from the British Library

Produced by Oriental Press Ltd.
Printed and bound in UAE